The Fun Book of Bible Trivia

The Fun Book of Bible Trivia

Robyn Martins

A BARBOUR BOOK

ISBN 1-55748-208-X

Published by   Barbour and Company, Inc.
                        P.O. Box 719
                        Uhrichsville, OH 44683

Printed in the United States of America

LET'S GET TRIVIAL!

Solomon had 700 wives and 300 concubines. Anniversaries must have been a problem.

The name Abraham (and Abram) is mentioned in the Bible 188 times. Sarah is only mentioned 31 times.

Adam was 130 years old when Seth was born. Genesis 5:3

Bethlehem means "house of bread."

Dodo was a descendant of Issachar. Who was Issachar? Why, the fifth son of Jacob and Leah, one of the 12 tribes of Israel. Judges 10:1, Genesis 30:17-18

Every three years Solomon's trading ships returned home with gold, silver, ivory, and a bunch of apes and baboons. Go figure. 1 Kings 10:22

Eliud was Jesus' great-great-great-grandfather.
Matthew 1:15

ARKTIFACTS AND MORE

Noah was a healthy 600 years old when God sent the flood. Genesis 7:6

A cubit is 18 inches long. That means the ark was 5400 inches long and 900 inches wide. Genesis 6:15

The ark was made of cypress wood (gopher wood in the King James Version). Genesis 6:14

Noah died at 950 years of age. Genesis 9:29

• • • • • • • • • • • • • •

Jacob and Rachel were cousins. Genesis 29:10

In the entire book of Esther, God is not mentioned once.

Job's first daughter of his second family was named Jemimah. Job 42:14

An omer is equivalent to 2 quarts.

Israelites were forbidden to wear clothes made of two kinds of material. So much for 50% cotton/50% polyester. Leviticus 19:19

When the Arameans were camped outside Samaria, God made the sound of chariots and horses and a big army to scare them away. It worked. 2 Kings 7:6-7

David's warriors could shoot arrows right and left handed. 1 Chronicles 12:2

Obed's grandma Naomi was his nurse when he was a baby. Ruth 4:6

• • • • • • • • • • • • • •

When King Xerxes couldn't sleep,
he had people read the record of
his reign to him. Esther 6:1

• • • • • • • • • • • • • •

Jews tried to stone Jesus at the temple. They failed, of course. John 8:59

After Saul killed himself, the Philistines cut off his head and hung it in a temple. 1 Chronicles 10:10

When the Ark was on its way back to Israel, God killed 70 men who got curious and looked inside it. 1 Samuel 6:19

Manna tasted like honey wafers. Exodus 16:31

In ancient Israel, men closed a deal by exchanging sandals. Ruth 4:7

The Levites had a mandatory retirement age of 50 years. Numbers 8:25

During a famine in Samaria, a donkey's head sold for 80 shekels of silver. 2 Kings 6:25

Moses' brother and sister were mad because he married a Cushite woman. Numbers 12:1

If a Hebrew person found a bird's nest full of birds, he could take the babies but had to leave the mother bird behind. Deuteronomy 22:7

Ham, Noah's son, built Nineveh. Genesis 10:11

After Moses was given the Ten Commandments, he wore a veil over his face because he glowed. Exodus 34:33-35

When Lot and his daughters moved out of Zoar, they lived in a cave. Genesis 19:30

When meat was being boiled for a sacrifice, the priest got to stick a fork in the pot and keep whatever it brought up. 1 Samuel 2:13

Elijah outran Ahab's chariots from Carmel all the way to Jezreel. 1 Kings 18:46

QUIZ TIME!

1. What is the shortest chapter in the Bible?

2. We all know about Shadrach, Meshach, and Abednego, but do you know their names before they were changed?

3. Who was chosen to replace Judas Iscariot after he you know what?

4. Who was turned down to fill Judas' place as disciple?

5. Who was Moses' father?

6. How old was Adam when he died?

7. What was Peter's name in Aramaic? And don't say "Rock."

8. Who was a "wild donkey of a man?"

9. Who did Jesus take with Him to the mountain where He was transfigured?

10. Who said, "Nazareth! Can anything good come from there?"

QUIZ ANSWERS

1. Psalm 117. It has two verses.

2. Hananiah, Mishael, and Azariah. Daniel 1:7

3. Matthias. Acts 1:23-26

4. Barsabbas a.k.a. Justus a.k.a. Joseph. Acts 1:23

5. Amram, with some dispute. Numbers 26:59.

6. 930 years old. Genesis 5:5

7. Cephas. John 1:42

8. Ishmael, Hagar's son. Genesis 16:12

9. Peter, James, and John. Matthew 17:1

10. Nathanael. John 1:46

What was the name of Ruth's sister-in-law?
Don't even think about looking it up.

Orpah. Ruth 1:4

WHAT'S IN A NAME?

The many names given to Jesus are familiar to most who have read the Bible, unless the consonants have been removed. Add the missing consonants to the vowels below to reveal some of Jesus' names.

Example: IAUEL = Immanuel

1. AA and OEA

2. I and I A

3. OO EE

4. I A

5. I of I

6. A of O

7. AE

8. IE of IE

9. OO of EE

10. UE IE

· · · · · · · · · · · · · ·

While you're thinking this over, finish Isaiah 9:6: "And he will be called. . ._____ _____, _____ _____, _____ _____, _____ ____ _____."

ANSWERS

1. Alpha and Omega. Revelation 1:11

2. Bright and Morning Star. Revelation 22:16

3. Good Shepherd. John 10:14

4. I Am. John 8:58

5. King of Kings. Revelation 19:16

6. Lamb of God. John 1:29

7. Master. John 1:38

8. Prince of Life. Acts 3:15

9. Root of Jesse. Isaiah 11:10

10. True Vine. John 15:1

• • • • • • • • • • • • •

Isaiah 9:6: And he will be called
Wonderful Counselor, Mighty God,
Everlasting Father, Prince of Peace.

Nine to Five

Demetrius was a silversmith. Acts 19:24

Paul was a tentmaker. Acts 18:1-3

Joseph, Mary's husband, was a carpenter. Matthew 13:15

Alexander was a metal worker. 2 Timothy 4:14

Luke was a medical doctor. Colossians 4:14

Lydia was a saleswoman. Acts 16:14

Zacchaeus was a tax collector. Luke 19:2

Tertullus was a lawyer. Acts 24:1

ODDS AND OMEGAS

Evidently, Amram and Jochebed didn't name their son. It was Pharaoh's daughter who called him Moses.
Exodus 2:10

Did you know that when Jesus died, saints rose from the dead and walked around Jerusalem? Matthew 27:52-53

There are a lot of "wolves in sheep's clothing" these days. But Jesus used the term to describe false prophets a couple thousand years ago. Matthew 7:15

The ultimate sarcasm: God described the people in Nineveh as not knowing their left from their right. Jonah 4:11

Ruth's first husband was Mahlon. Ruth 4:10

They had peanut butter in the Bible—Ezekiel's tongue was stuck to the roof of his mouth until the Lord gave him words. Ezekiel 3:26-27

Animals have to answer to God, too. Genesis 9:5

Paul was beaten five times and shipwrecked three.
2 Corinthians 11:24-25

WHO SAID. . .?

1. "Lord, why can't I follow you now? I lay down my life for you."

2. "Indeed, women have been kept from us. . ."

3. "You son of a perverse and rebellious woman!"

4. "From now on all generations will call me blessed."

5. "After I am worn out and my master is old, will I now have this pleasure?"

6. "Even up to half the kingdom, it will be given you."

7. "Look, your sister-in-law is going back to her people and her gods. Go back with her."

8. "...whatever comes out of the door of my house to meet me when I return in triumph from the Ammonites will be the Lord's, and I will sacrifice it as a burnt offering."

9. "...The joy of the Lord is your strength."

10. "What have I done to you to make you beat me these three times?"

THEY DID!

1. Peter. John 13:37

2. David. 1 Samuel 21:5

3. King Saul. 1 Samuel 20:30

4. Mary. Luke 1:48

5. Sarah. Genesis 18:12

6. King Xerxes. Esther 5:3; and Herod. Mark 6:23

7. Naomi. Ruth 1:15

8. Jephthah. Judges 11:30

9. Nehemiah. Nehemiah 8:10

10. Balaam's donkey. Numbers 22:28

? What did John the Baptist eat?
Locusts and wild honey. Matthew 3:4

A TRIVIAL WORDSEARCH

It isn't much fun playing with familiar names and places. Where's the challenge in finding a word like Judah or Bethlehem? So, here is a true challenge—20 cities mentioned here and there in the Old Testament. If you can find them all, give yourself a bowl of raspberry sherbet. If you can find them on a map, give yourself a roundtrip ticket to Ziklag.

```
B T E B H E S H B O N
G A R A A L U Z N A I
M B M M R T B O U L B
A E D O R O E E Z U L
T Z E T V L J H T A E
T I T H N A N J B A A
A K A L H D U M A H M
N L J A A Z A H I A R
A A R K R C H J K N A
H G A B A F O G B E C
B I Z E N N P F E S H
```

Abez	Luz	Dumah	Hanes
Ijon	Dor	Eltolad	Jebus
Mattanah	Hara	Ibleam	Ono
Heshbon	Bamoth	Jaazah	Etam
Gaba	Ithnan	Nezib	Ziklag

WORDSEARCH SOLUTION

●●●●●●●●●●●●●

The three magi were never actually at the traditional manger scene. They saw Jesus a little later at Joseph and Mary's house. Matthew 2:11

For Better or for Worse
Clue: We're All Married Couples

1. After we gave a little money to the apostles and put some more in our pockets, we fell on the floor, so to speak.

2. We moved from Italy to Corinth and made tents with Paul.

3. We traveled a lot and started our very own nation.

4. We first met in a grain field, cold feet and all.

5. Our first son died as a baby, but our second son was a royally smart guy.

6. We had three children with funny names, and after a short separation, rejoined at an auction block.

7. We ate quite often and were the end of that nasty Haman.

8. We ran for our lives at the warning of two angels, but one of us didn't quite make it.

9. We prayed to God for a son, and He gave us Samuel.

10. John the Baptist thought we shouldn't be married, so we snuffed him out.

THE HAPPY COUPLES

1. Ananias and Sapphira. Acts 5:1ff

2. Aquila and Priscilla. Acts 18:23

3. Abraham and Sarah. Genesis 12:1-2

4. Ruth and Boaz. Ruth 3:7-8

5. David and Bathsheba. 2 Samuel 12:5-24

6. Hosea and Gomer. Hosea 1-3

7. Esther and King Xerxes.   Esther 5-7

8. Lot and his wife (name not given). Genesis 19

9. Elkanah and Hannah. 1 Samuel 1:2

10. Herod and Herodias. Matthew 14:3

• • • • • • • • • • • • •

The iron point alone on Goliath's spear weighed about 15 pounds. 1 Samuel 17:7

TRUE / FALSE

Pencils ready?

1. Abram traveled with his father away from his home in Uz.

2. God said to Noah, "Whoever sheds the blood of man, by man shall his blood be shed..."

3. Peter baptized Lydia in Philippi.

4. Isaac told people that his wife was his sister to save his skin.

5. Joseph was 23 when his brothers sold him to the Ishmaelites.

6. Jesus fed 4000 people with a few loaves of bread and some fish.

7. Moses and Abraham appeared with Jesus on the Mount of Transfiguration.

8. Samson was a judge over Israel for 20 years.

9. The clothes of John the Baptist were made of goat skin.

10. Lazarus had been in his tomb for three days when Jesus called him out.

T/F ANSWERS

1. False. Abram was from Ur, not Uz. Genesis 11:31

2. True. Genesis 9:6

3. False. Paul baptized Lydia. Acts 16:15

4. True. So did his father Abraham. Genesis 26:7

5. False. He was 17. Genesis 37:2

6. True. Even though most people only talk about the 5000 people, this is still amazing. Matthew 15:29-39

7. False. Moses and Elijah appeared with him. Matthew 17:3

8. True. Judges 16:31

9. Get real. They were made of camel's hair. Matthew 3:4

10. False. He was in his tomb for four days. Remember, Martha was afraid he would smell. John 11:39

• • • • • • • • • • • • • • •

Herod was struck down by God, and his body was eaten by worms. Acts 13:23

Zany Miscellany

Jair, a judge of Israel, had 30 sons who rode 30 donkeys, and controlled 30 towns.   Judges 10:3-4

and

Ibzan, a judge, had 30 sons and 30 daughters. Judges 12:9

and

Abdon, another judge, had 40 sons and 30 grandsons who rode on 70 donkeys. Judges 12:14

The familiar story of Jesus saying, "If any one of you is without sin, let him be the first to throw a stone at her" (John 7:53-8:11) is found nowhere else in the Bible. In fact, it isn't even found in many manuscripts of the Gospels.

Abraham's father was named Terah. Genesis 11:26

The term "scapegoat" comes from the use of a goat that was to receive the sins of the people and be released into the wilderness. Leviticus 16:10

Thomas, the one who is always ridiculed for skepticism, is also known as Didymus. John 20:24

You may have heard people exclaim, "Jehoshaphat!" Well, Jehoshaphat is the valley where God will judge the nations according to Joel 3:2. It's also the name of the fourth king of Judah.

Jezebel was so bad that she had Naboth stoned to death just to get his vineyard. 1 Kings 21:1-16

Moses was four months old when Pharaoh's daughter found him in the basket. Acts 7:20-21

When Paul was in a shipwreck off the shore of Malta, there were 276 people on board. Acts 27:37

• • • • • • • • • • • •

Nahor, Abraham's grandfather, means "snorer."

• • • • • • • • • • • •

When Lazarus came out of the grave, only his hands, feet, and face were wrapped with cloth. John 11:44

When Elizabeth was pregnant with John the Baptist, Zecharias was struck dumb until the baby was born. Luke 1

Moses had two wives, Zipporah and a Cushite woman. Exodus 2:21 and Numbers 12:1

EMBATTLED HYMNS

Decipher these Scripture excerpts to find inspirations for some of our favorite hymns.

1. . . .BUEV,BUEV, BUEV, EUSA PUA CEFDPBNZ.

2. . . .XTAMS BDH IDTPH VUX IDEE MDTA SJMXPJ.

3. D QTUI NBCN FV SJAJJFJS EDOJNB.

4. PEUSDUXH NBDTPH CSJ HWUQJT UM NBJJ. . .

ANSWERS

1. Holy, holy, holy, Lord God almighty. Revelation 4:8

2. Under his wings you will find refuge. Psalm 91:4

3. I know that my redeemer liveth. Job 19:25

4. Glorious things of thee are spoken. Psalm 87:3

> **?** Of course, Jacob had 12 sons, but who was his only daughter?
>
> *Dinah, the one who was defiled by Shechem and caused such an uproar. Genesis 34:1*

22

ELIJAH/ELISHA

Elijah, Elisha, Elisha, Elijah. Which one was which? That's easy, but your job is to decide who did what. Fill in the blanks.

1. After he warned Ahab of a drought, _____ hid by a river and got food from birds, ravens to be exact.

2. Some prophets yelled, "There is death in the pot! Then, _____ put some flour in the stew, and everything was O.K.

3. Twenty loaves of barley bread fed 100 people when _____ told a man to feed them.

4. Some kids called _____ a baldhead. So, he cursed them.

5. The widow at Zarephath had a son who stopped breathing, so _____ prayed and brought him back to life.

6. _____ made fun of the prophets of Asherah when they couldn't get Baal to start a fire.

7. Someone lost an axe head in the Jordan River. So, _____ made it float.

8. When _____ prayed, God made a whole band of enemy Arameans blind.

9. _____ gave a widow jar after jar of oil to pay her bills.

10. _____ was a Tishbite.

WHO'S WHO?

1. Elijah. 1 Kings 17:5

2. Elisha. 2 Kings 4:38-41

3. Elisha. 2 Kings 4:44

4. Elisha. 2 Kings 2:23

5. Elijah. 1 Kings 17:17-23

6. Elijah. 1 Kings 18:27

7. Elisha. 2 Kings 6:1-7

8. Elisha. 2 Kings 6:18

9. Elisha. 2 Kings 4:1-7

10. Elijah. 1 Kings 17:1

WAR AND PIECES

Joseph's tribe was split in two. His sons Ephraim and Manasseh got their own land allotments. Joshua 16:4

With Nehemiah as the foreman, it took 52 days to rebuild Jerusalem's wall. Nehemiah 6:15

Stephen was the first recorded Christian martyr. He was stoned to death. Acts 7:59-60

• • • • • • • • • • • •

Israelites weren't allowed to eat camels.
What a sacrifice! Well, actually, they
couldn't sacrifice them either.
Leviticus 11:4

• • • • • • • • • • • •

When Joshua's army was taking over parts of Canaan, they crippled their enemy's horses by clipping their hamstrings. Joshua 11:9

When Saul couldn't get his armor-bearer to kill him, he committed suicide by falling on his own sword.
1 Samuel 31:4

Antipas was a martyr who lived in Pergamum, one of the Asian cities named in Revelation. Revelation 2:13

When Pharaoh gave orders to kill all Hebrew baby boys, Shiphrah and Puah, two Hebrew midwives, refused to do it. Exodus 1:15

When God finally spoke to Job, he spoke from out of a storm. Job 38: 1, 40:6

Joshua made the Gibeonites be woodcutters and water carriers for the Israelites as a curse. Joshua 9:23

Joseph, Mary, and Jesus moved to Egypt for awhile because Herod wanted to kill Jesus. Matthew 2:13

Esau's third wife, Mahalath, was also his cousin Ishmael's daughter. Genesis 28:9

? Jonah wasn't the only one sent to Nineveh. What other prophet ministered there?

Nahum. Nahum 1:1

Moses had two sons, Gershom and Eliezer. Exodus 18:3

Samson set the tails of 300 foxes on fire and set the poor animals loose in some Philistine grain fields.
Judges 15:4-5

In Old Testament times people wore sackcloth so other people would know they were in mourning. 2 Samuel 3:31

WHERE DO YOU FIND IT, ANYWAY?

Below are some familiar Bible passages that people often like to quote. They aren't necessarily trivial, but their references aren't as easily recognized. So, where do you find them, anyway?

1. Jesus wept.

2. There is no one righteous, not even one.

3. They will soar on wings like eagles; they will run and not grow weary, they will walk and not be faint.

4. The Lord is my shepherd, I shall not be in want.

5. For the wages of sin is death, but the gift of God is eternal life in Christ Jesus our Lord.

6. A man reaps what he sows.

7. Glory to God in the highest, and on earth peace to men on whom his favor rests.

8. There is a time for everything, and a season for every activity under heaven.

9. Let my people go, so that they may worship me.

10. This cup is the new covenant in my blood, which is poured out for you.

OPEN YOUR BIBLES

1. John 11:35

2. Romans 13:10

3. Isaiah 40:31b

4. Too easy! Psalm 23:1

5. Romans 6:23

6. Galatians 6:7

7. Luke 2:14

8. Ecclesiastes 3:1

9. Exodus 8:1

10. Luke 22:20

• • • • • • • • • • • • •

Locusts, katydids, crickets, and grasshoppers
were considered clean food for the Israelites.
What's for lunch? Leviticus 11:22

Quiz Time!

1. What was Achan's sin?

2. Why did Paul shave his head?

3. What evangelist had four daughters who prophesied?

4. James and John were the sons of Zebedee, but who was their mother?

5. Who put Jesus in the tomb?

6. What was the Ethiopian eunuch reading when he met Philip?

7. What was the answer to Samson's riddle, "Out of the eater, something to eat; out of the strong, something sweet."

8. When Jesus wept, why did he weep, or what was the occasion?

9. Moses made a bronze snake. For what was it an antidote?

10. Methuselah lived longer than anyone else recorded in the Bible. Who came in second?

QUIZ ANSWERS

1. He took some devoted things from Jericho. Joshua 7:1

2. It marked the end of a vow he had taken. Acts 18:18

3. Philip. Acts 21:8-9

4. Salome. Mark 15:40

5. Joseph of Arimathea and Nicodemus. John 19:38-39

6. The Book of Isaiah. Acts 8:28

7. Honey from a lion's carcass. Judges 14:14

8. The lack of faith of his followers, or Lazarus' death. John 11:35

9. The bite of venomous snakes. Numbers 21:4-9

10. Jared, Methuselah's grandfather. Genesis 5:20

Esoteric Rhetoric

King Jehoshaphat built a fleet of trading ships that were wrecked before they ever set sail. 1 Kings 22:48

When Nineveh repented, its residents even put sackcloth on all their animals. Jonah 3:8

Meshech, the grandson of Shem, was also known as Mash (Hebrew). Wouldn't you use a different name, too?
1 Chronicles 1:17

Job had 3000 camels, at first. Job 1:3

Whole books are dedicated to the escapades of the kings of Israel and Judah. But did you know that Judah once had a ruling queen? Queen Athaliah ruled for six years.
2 Kings 11:3

Mordecai acted as Esther's father, but he was really her cousin. Esther 2:7

Isaiah wrote with an ordinary pen, as opposed to an unusual one. Isaiah 8:1

The Israelites called their communities together by blowing two silver trumpets. Numbers 10:23

HOT STUFF
(OR HOW FIRE WAS USED IN THE OLD TESTAMENT)

The burning bush was obviously on fire. Exodus 3:2

A pillar of fire led Israel at night. Exodus 13:21

Elijah was taken by a chariot and horses of fire. 2 Kings 2:11

Sodom and Gomorrah were destroyed by fire.
Genesis 19:24

The Lord descended on Mt. Sinai with fire. Exodus 19:18

Twice, "fire from Heaven" consumed a captain and 50 men
who were a threat to Elijah. 2 Kings 1:9-12

Fire consumed the outskirts of the camp when the Israelites
wouldn't stop whining. Numbers 11:11

"Fire of God" destroyed Job's sheep and servants. Job 1:16

Fire killed 250 men after they opposed Moses and Aaron.
Numbers 16:35

THE PLAGUES

(OR, HOW REAL ESTATE PLUMMETED IN EGYPT)

Name the plagues God sent to Egypt to convince them to
"Let my people go!" They must be in order to get full credit.

1.

2.

3.

4.

5.

7.

8.

9.

10.

THE PLAGUES IN ORDER
(EXODUS 7:14 TO CHAPTER 11)

1. The Nile was turned into blood.

2. Frogs came from water.

3. Dust was turned into gnats.

4. Flies were everywhere.

5. All the livestock died.

6. Everybody had boils.

7. Hail destroyed the crops.

8. Locusts ate what the hail missed.

9. There were three straight days of darkness.

10. The first born son of every family died.

? Who succeeded Solomon as King of Israel?

Rehoboam, his son. 2 Chronicles 9:31

AND GOD SAID. . .

To whom did God say the following:

1. I will make your offspring like the dust of the earth, so that if anyone could count the dust, then your offspring could be counted.

2. Two nations are in your womb, and two peoples from within you will be separated.

3. Your house and your kingdom will endure forever before me; your throne will be established forever.

4. I will heal you . . . I will add 15 years to your life.

5. Whom shall I send? And who will go for us?

6. Before I formed you in the womb I knew you, before you were born I set you apart.

7. There is no one on earth like him; he is blameless and upright, a man who fears God and shuns evil.

8. Let the water teem with living creatures, and let birds fly above the earth. . . .

9. Take off your sandals, for the place where you are standing is holy ground.

10. Go, take to yourself an adulterous wife and children of unfaithfulness. . . .

GOD SPOKE TO. . .

1. Abram. Genesis 13:16

2. Rebekah. Genesis 25:23a

3. David. 2 Samuel 7:16-17

4. Hezekiah via Isaiah. 2 Kings 20:5-6

5. Isaiah. Isaiah 6:8

6. Jeremiah. Jeremiah 1:5

7. Satan about Job. Job 1:8

8. The earth. Genesis 1:20

9. Moses. Exodus 3:5

10. Hosea. 1:2

• • • • • • • • • • • • •

*Illyricum, a place Paul once mentioned, is
actually Albania and Yugoslavia.
Romans 15:19*

WHAT DOES IT MEAN, ANYWAY?

Amen means "so let it be."

Selah? Nobody really knows, but it was probably a musical term. Psalm 3:2

An ephah is a dry measure of more than half a bushel. Ezekiel 45:10

Onycha is an expensive incense like musk that Moses used. Exodus 30:34

Goad or oxgoad: a wooden pole used to clean plows and prod animals. Judges 3:31

A handstaff is a staff in the hand. What did you think? Ezekiel 39:9 (KJV)

Crisping pins were purses. Isaiah 3:22

Nitre is a baking soda-type stuff used to make soap. Proverbs 25:20

A withe is a strong twig (a thong in the NIV). Judges 16:7-9

OFF THE RECORD

Shem, Noah's son, was the ancestor of the Jewish people. Genesis 11:10-26

Abraham's servant went all the way to Mesopotamia to find a wife for Isaac. Genesis 24:10

It didn't rain in the Garden of Eden, or out of it for that matter. Water came up from the ground to make things grow. Genesis 2:5-6

Gideon laid out the fleece looking for a sign from the Lord because he wanted to beat the Midianites in battle the next day. Judges 6:36-40

• • • • • • • • • • • • •

Job's wife thought he had bad breath. Job 19:17

• • • • • • • • • • • • •

Solomon was called Solomon until the day he died, but when he was born, God named him Jedidiah.
2 Samuel 12:25

Daniel and his friends ate nothing but vegetables and water for ten days. Daniel 1:12

The Ammonites tried to embarrass David's men by shaving off half their beard and cutting off their clothes at about mid-buttocks length. It must have worked. 2 Samuel 10:4

AN ANIMAL WORDSEARCH

The Bible is full of animals. They were ridden, slaughtered, talked to, and even listened to. In Psalm 80 Asaph wrote about an animal who ravaged the "vine out of Egypt." What was it? Hint: It's hidden in the wordsearch twice.

```
C A M R G A B A T S E
O B O A R W E A S E L
R O R O E L H U L Y E
A A E Z Y K E O N E V
L R B C H A M O I S I
H O O P O E O R A E A
I A P N U L T H A R T
N S W I N E H P Z M H
D P L C D S A T Y R A
C B I P Y G A R G E N
Z E B O I M C O N E Y
```

Behemoth	Chamois	Coney
Greyhound	Hart	Leviathan
Mole	Pygarg	Roe
Satyr	Weasel	Asp
Coral	Swine	Hind
Zeboim	Boar	Bats

ANIMAL WORDSEARCH SOLUTION

The animal that ravaged the "vine out of Egypt"
was a BOAR.

STAFF ONLY

*And God said, "But take this STAFF in your hand
so you can perform miraculous signs with it."*
Exodus 4:17

When Moses threw it on the ground it turned into a snake,
and he ran away from it. Exodus 4:4

It turned into a snake again in front of Pharaoh.
Exodus 7:10

Most of the plagues in Egypt were brought on with the staff.

Moses divided the Red Sea with it. Exodus 14:16

Moses hit the rock of Horeb with it to get water.
Exodus 17:6

Aaron's staff budded and produced almonds.
Numbers 17:8

Moses hit a rock twice to get water, even though he was just
supposed to talk to the thing. Numbers 25:11

HELP ME RHODA
(AND A FEW OTHER GOLDEN OLDIES)

Rhoda was the servant girl who answered the door when Peter escaped from jail. Acts 12:13

Phoebe was a deacon who was highly valued by Paul. She may have even delivered the letter to the Romans.
Romans 16:1-2

Abigail saved her silly husband from David's wrath, and after the guy died, she married David. 1 Samuel 25

Anna was an 84-year-old prophet who praised God for the baby Jesus at the Temple in Jerusalem. Luke 2:36-38

Junias was an apostle who was once imprisoned with Paul.
Romans 16:7

Huldah warned of impending judgment of Judah.
2 Kings 22:14

Joanna was one of the women who discovered that Jesus had risen and left the tomb. Luke 24:10

DISCIPLE MATCH-UP

AS LISTED IN LUKE 6:14-16

Match them up with their a.k.a.'s, relations, or otherwise brief descriptions.

1. Simon Peter

2. Andrew

3. James

4. John

5. Philip

6. Bartholomew

7. Matthew

8. Thomas

9. James the less

10. Simon (Zealot)

11. Judas

12. Judas Iscariot

a. Alphaeus' son

b. Also called Thaddaeus

c. Andrew's brother

d. A friend of Bartholomew's

e. Also called Levi

f. James' brother

g. Also called Didymus

h. Son of a Simon

i. Also called the Cananaen

j. Simon Peter's brother

k. John's brother

l. Also called Nathanael

MATCHED-UP DISCIPLES

1. c. Simon Peter and Andrew were brothers.

2. j. Ditto.

3. k. James and John were brothers.

4. f. Ditto.

5. d. Philip and Bartholomew were friends.

6. l. Bartholomew was also called Nathanael.

7. e. Matthew was also called Levi.

8. g. Thomas was also called Didymus.

9. a. James the less was Alphaeus' son.

10. i. Simon the Zealot was once called a Cananaen.

11. b. Judas was also called Thaddaeus.

12. h. Judas Iscariot was the son of a Simon. There are so many.

THE BACK FORTY

(WAY BACK WHEN!)

Jonah told Nineveh that in 40 days the city would be overturned. Jonah 3:4

Jesus fasted for 40 days in the desert. Matthew 4:2 says, "...he was hungry." Imagine that.

After the Resurrection, Jesus was on earth for 40 days. Acts 1:3

Moses was 40 years old when he first visited the Israelites in Egypt. Acts 7:23

He was another 40 years older when he saw the burning bush. Acts 7:30

And, he was another 40 years older when he died. Deuteronomy 34:7

Goliath challenged the Israelites twice a day for 40 days. 1 Samuel 17:16

While Deborah judged Israel, the people lived in peace for 40 years. Behind every peaceful country, there is a good woman. Judges 5:31

There were also 40 years of peace under Gideon's judgeship. Judges 8:38

DROUGHT, ANYONE?

The Israelites crossed the Red Sea on dry ground, of course. But this miracle was repeated a few more times on occasions that evidently don't rate a Hollywood effort.

The Israelites crossed the Jordan with the ark of the covenant. Joshua 4:7

Elijah divided the Jordan with his coat, of all things. 2 Kings 2:8

Elisha was left with Elijah's coat and used it to part the Jordan again. 2 Kings 2:14

The Lord will split the Euphrates into seven streams "so that men can cross in sandals" (Isaiah 11:15) or high-tops, depending on the times.

THE FULL ARMOR OF GOD

"Therefore put on the full armor of God, so that when the day of evil comes, you may be able to stand your ground. . . ." Ephesians 6:13

Fill in the blanks:

1. Belt of _____.

2. Breastplate of _____.

3. Feet fitted with _____.

4. Shield of _____.

5. Helmet of _____.

6. Sword of _____.

ANSWERS

1. Belt of TRUTH.

2. Breastplate of RIGHTEOUSNESS.

3. Feet fitted with READINESS.

4. Shield of FAITH.

5. Helmet of SALVATION.

6. Sword of THE SPIRIT.

• • • • • • • • • • • • •

*The disciples were first called Christians
in Antioch. Acts 11:26*

FACTS IT TO ME

The covering for the tabernacle was made out of ram skins and sea cow hides. Exodus 36:19

Joseph's brothers didn't sell him directly to the Egyptians. They sold him to some Midianites who sold him to Potiphar in Egypt. Genesis 38:36

When Elisha learned that Jericho had bad water, he made it better by tossing in about a bowl full of salt water. 2 Kings 2:21

•••••••••••

People weren't given permission to eat meat until after the Flood. Genesis 9:3

•••••••••••

The Gospel of Luke and the book of Acts were both written to somebody named Theophilus.

Once Ezekiel was sitting in his house when a big hand picked him up by the hair of his head and took him somewhere between heaven and earth. Ezekiel 8:3

For years the Israelites burned incense to the bronze snake that Moses made, until Hezekiah broke it up. 2 Kings 18:4

King Saul's wife was named Ahinoam. 1 Samuel 14:50

FIRST THINGS FIRST

Cain built the first city. 4:17

Jubal was the father of people who play harps and flutes. 4:21

Cain committed the first murder. 4:8

Noah planted the first vineyard. 9:20

Lamech was the first polygamist. 4:19

Abel was the first shepherd. 4:2

Cain was the first farmer. 4:2

Tubal-cain was the first iron worker. Did he start the union, too? 4:22

Abram was the first Hebrew. 13:14

ALL SHOOK UP

Rearrange the "all shook up" letters below to spell some of the kings. Then decide whether they ruled Israel or Judah.

1. MHOBOARE

2. SABAAH

3. SHPHTHJEOAA

4. HHEOAJAZ

5. AAAMIZH

6. SMALULH

7. KAHAHIEP

8. SHAIJO

9. LAATHIHA

10. DEEKIHAZ

ANSWERS

1. King Rehoboam of Judah

2. King Baasha of Israel

3. King Jehoshaphat of Judah

4. King Jehoahaz of Israel

5. King Amaziah of Judah

6. King Shallum of Israel

7. King Pekahiah of Israel

8. King Josiah of Judah

9. Queen Athaliah of Judah

10. King Zedekiah of Judah

• • • • • • • • • • • •

*King Ahab disguised himself in a battle
so the enemy wouldn't try to kill him, but a random
arrow hit him anyway. 1 Kings 22:29-35*

BLIND SPOTS

"Apple of your eye" is hardly a new expression. Solomon said it in Proverbs 7:2.

The Sabbath was measured from the evening of one day to the evening of the next. Leviticus 23:32

When Stephen spoke to the Sanhedrin, he gave a history lesson from Abraham all the way to Solomon. It was the first recorded filibuster. Acts 7:1-47

? "An eye for an eye" was an Old Testament rule of thumb. What was Jesus' rule for responding to an offense?

Turn the other cheek. Matthew 5:38-39

Haman had a gallows built to hang Mordecai, but he was hanged on it instead. Esther 7:9

Here's a phrase that has stood the test of time—Job was the first recorded person to say "the skin of my teeth." Job 19:20

When Moses led the Israelites out of Egypt, he took Joseph's bones. Exodus 13:19

John was on the island of Patmos when he wrote Revelation. Revelation 1:9

THIRD TIME'S THE CHARM

Jonah was inside the big fish for three days. Jonah 1:17

Peter denied Christ three times. Matthew 26:34

Jesus rose after three days. John 2:19

Paul was blind for three days. Acts 9:9

Esther fasted for three days before she spoke to the King.
Esther 4:16

Isaiah went around stripped and barefoot for three years as
a sign against Egypt. Isaiah 20:3

Elijah stretched himself out over a widow's son three times
to bring him back to life. 1 Kings 17:21

POP QUIZ

Name the fathers of all these people.

1. Seth.

2. Isaiah.

3. Ham.

4. Boaz.

5. Joseph (Mary's husband).

6. Jonah.

7. Samson.

8. Noah.

9. Lot.

10. Sarah.

ANSWERS

1. Adam begat Seth. Genesis 4:25

2. Amoz begat Isaiah. Isaiah 1:1

3. Noah begat Ham. Genesis 5:32

4. Salmon begat Boaz. Matthew 1:5

5. Jacob begat Joseph, Mary's husband. Matthew 1:16

6. Amittai begat Jonah. Jonah 1:1

7. Manoah begat Samson. Judges 13:2

8. Lamech begat Noah. Genesis 5:29

9. Haran begat Lot. Genesis 11:27

10. Terah begat Sarah. Genesis 20:12

TRUE / FALSE

1. In Pharaoh's dream seven gaunt cows ate seven sleek cows.

2. King Herod gave the head of John the Baptist to his wicked wife.

3. King Belshazzar had Daniel tossed in the lions' den.

4. Solomon was made king before David died.

5. Jesus was 33 years old when He started His ministry.

6. Noah's son Japheth was older than his brother Shem.

7. After Jesus left the tomb, the first person who saw Him was John.

8. It took Elisha just one try to set fire to his drenched sacrifice.

9. Aaron died on Mount Hor, after he gave his clothes to his son.

10. Elisha saw Elijah take off from west of the Jordan River.

ANSWERS

1. True. Genesis 41:4

2. False. He gave it to his stepdaughter. Matthew 14:6-11

3. False. It was King Darius. Daniel 6

4. True. 1 Kings 1:43

5. False. He was about 30 years old. Luke 3:23

6. True. Genesis 10:21

7. False. Mary Magdalene saw him first. Mark 16:9

8. False. It was Elijah who prayed for fire to burn the bull. 1 Kings 18:36-37

9. True. Numbers 20:28

10. False. They were on the east side. 2 Kings 2:8

Who did Pontius Pilate release to the Jews instead of Jesus?

Barabbas, a murderer. Mark 15:15

KING ME!

(CHECK(ER) IT OUT)

Solomon's traders imported horses and chariots from Egypt.
2 Chronicles 1:17

Eglon, king of Moab, was so fat that when Ehud stabbed him with a one and a half foot long sword, the handle sank into his belly. Judges 3:22

Esther's Hebrew name was Hadassah. Esther 2:7

When Paul and Barnabas were speaking in Lystra, they were mistaken for the gods Hermes and Zeus by people in the crowd. Acts 14:12

? What were the names of Job's three "friends?"

Eliphaz, Bildad, and Zophar. Job 2:11

Jacob changed his youngest son's name from Ben-oni, chosen by Rachel, to Benjamin. Genesis 35:18

When Abraham told people that Sarah was his sister, he was only half lying. They had the same father.
Genesis 20:12

When David crept up behind Saul and cut off a corner of his robe, did you know that Saul was actually relieving himself? 1 Samuel 24:3-4

When Paul was building a fire, a poisonous snake bit him on the hand. People thought he was a god when he didn't die. Acts 28:1-6

Jerusalem was once called Jebus. Judges 19:10

The Sea of Galilee was also known as the Sea of Tiberias. John 21:1

Timothy was raised by his grandmother, Lois, and his mother, Eunice. 2 Timothy 1:5

Solomon had 12,000 horses. 1 Kings 10:26

? What are the four rivers in the Garden of Eden?

Pishon, Gihon, Tigris, and Euphrates. Genesis 2:11-14

Do you remember the Midianite woman and the Israelite man that Phinehas killed with a stake? They were Cozbi, daughter of Zur, and Zimri, son of Salu, respectively. Numbers 25:14-15

Isaac was 40 years old when he married Rebekah. Genesis 25:20

Jericho was the City of Palms. Judges 1:16

J - WALK

Fill in the blanks to complete the words that are described. Obviously, they all start with the letter J.

1. J_ _ _ _ _. A river east of the Jordan where Jacob met an angel.

2. J_ _ _ _ _ _ _. A famous son of King Saul.

3. J_ _ _ _ _ _-J_ _ _ _. Abraham almost sacrificed Isaac there.

4. J_ _ _ _ _ _ _. An Israelite judge who sacrificed his daughter.

5. J_ _ _ _ _ _. A city with a lot of history, it fell down after a week-long siege.

6. J_ _ _ _ _ _. Jezebel was eaten by dogs in this city.

7. J_ _ _ _ _ _ _. She put her baby in a basket to save his life.

8. J_ _ _ _ _ _ _. A prophet under Josiah, king of Judah.

9. J_ _ _. A prophet whose name meant "The Lord is God."

10. J_ _ _ _. The father of Bukki. Hint: See Numbers 34:22.

J NAMES

1. Jabbok. Genesis 32:22-30

2. Jonathan. 1 Samuel 13:16

3. Jehovah-Jireh. Genesis 22:14

4. Jephthah. Judges 11:39

5. Jericho. Joshua 6:20

6. Jezreel. 2 Kings 9:36

7. Jochebed. Exodus 2:3

8. Jeremiah. Jeremiah 1:1-2

9. Joel. Joel 1:1

10. Jogli. Numbers 34:22

THE BEATITUDES
MATTHEW 5:3-10

These words are anything but trivial, but blessed are you if you can complete each phrase.

1. Blessed are the poor in spirit,. . . .

2. Blessed are those who mourn,. . . .

3. Blessed are the meek,. . . .

4. Blessed are those who hunger and thirst for righteousness,. . . .

5. Blessed are the merciful,. . . .

6. Blessed are the pure in heart,. . . .

7. Blessed are the peacemakers,. . . .

8. Blessed are those who are persecuted because of righteousness,. . . .

THE REST OF THE BEATITUDES

1. . . .for theirs is the kingdom of heaven.

2. . . .for they will be comforted.

3. . . .for they will inherit the earth.

4. . . .for they will be filled.

5. . . .for they will be shown mercy.

6. . . .for they will see God.

7. . . .for they will be called sons of God.

8. . . .for theirs is the kingdom of heaven.

? Where was Jonah trying to go when he ran away from his responsibilities in Nineveh?

Tarshish, Jonah 1:3

TRY TO REMEMBER

When the Israelites needed to relieve themselves, they had to go outside the camp and dig a hole.
Deuteronomy 23:12-13

The Exodus probably took place in 1446 B.C.

Psalm 119 is the longest chapter in the Bible with 176 verses.

Abraham had two nephews named Uz and Buz.
Genesis 22:21

Peter paid taxes for Jesus and himself with money he found in a fish's mouth. Not so trivial, but pretty strange.
Matthew 17:27

Everybody always says "Jesus fed five thousand," but that didn't include women and children. How about "Jesus fed the whole bunch." Matthew 14:21

The Philistine rulers each offered Delilah 1100 shekels of silver for telling them the secret of Samson's strength.
Judges 16:5

After the Resurrection, when Jesus told the disciples to put their fishing nets on the right side of the boat, they caught 153 fish. John 21:11

FORTY CARATS

The Flood, of course. Water flooded the earth for 40 days.
Genesis 7:17

Moses was on Mount Sinai 40 days receiving instructions
from God. Exodus 24:18

For some reason, it took 40 days to embalm a person back
when Jacob was alive, or actually when Jacob was dead.
Genesis 50:3

The Israelites ate manna for 40 years until they finally
settled in Canaan. Exodus 16:35

The representatives of each Israelite tribe explored Canaan
for 40 days before returning with their report to Moses.
Numbers 13:25

After the Israelites put the nix on conquering Canaan, they
were forced to wander in the desert for 40 years.
Numbers 32:13

Saul, David, Solomon, and Joash all reigned as kings for 40
years.

Elijah traveled for 40 days until he reached Horeb.
1 Kings 19:8

PROPHETS SHMOPHETS

1. This prophet asked if a leopard could change his spots.

2. This one saw a flying scroll in a vision.

3. Who talks about the "sword of the Lord?"

4. This prophet ate a scroll. Hopefully, it was just a vision.

5. A seraph touched this prophet's mouth with a hot coal.

6. He made an axe head float in water.

7. Who was slapped in the face for calling one of King Ahab's prophets a liar?

8. This prophet wrote the shortest book of the Old Testament.

9. This one lost his shade tree to a hungry worm.

10. He was a shepherd and a fig-tree gardener.

ANSWERS

1. Jeremiah. Jeremiah 13:23

2. Zechariah saw a scroll 30 feet long and 15 feet wide. Zechariah 5:1-3

3. Isaiah. Isaiah 34:6

4. Ezekiel had the tasty treat. Ezekiel 3:3

5. Isaiah again. Isaiah 6:6-7

6. Elisha. 2 Kings 6:6

7. Micaiah was slapped. 1 Kings 22:24

8. Obadiah. Obadiah (all 21 verses)

9. Jonah. Jonah 4:6-8

10. Amos. Amos 7:14

? According to Solomon's proverb, what is in Wisdom's right and left hands?

Long life is in the right and riches and honor are in the left. Proverbs 3:16

WHO AM I?

Fill in the blanks and unscramble the letters found in parentheses. The Gospel of Luke was written to this person.

1. I am the grandfather of Moab and Ben-Ammi. Come to think of it, I'm the father, too. __ __ (__)

2. My husband didn't love me very much. Was it because my eyes were weak? __ (__) __ (__)

3. I ate at David's table, and I was crippled in both feet.
   __ __ (__) __ __ (__) __ __ __ __

4. I visited Solomon and gave him all kinds of presents. What a guy! __ __ __ __ __ __ __ __ (__) __ __ __

5. King David gave me everything that belonged to Mephibosheth who had betrayed him. __ __ __ __

6. As king of Judah, I ousted my grandmother from the throne because she made a pagan idol. __ __ __

7. Some eunuchs threw me from my window, and dogs just ate me up. __ __ __ __ __ (__)

8. I was a "wee little man" in Jericho.
   __ __ __ __ __ __ (__) __

9. I traveled with Paul after his little tiff with Barnabas. __ (__) __ __

10. Paul left me with those Cretans who are "always liars, evil brutes, lazy gluttons." __ __ __ (__)

THE WHO

1. Lot. Genesis 19:36-38

2. Leah. Genesis 29:16

3. Mephibosheth. 2 Samuel 9

4. The Queen of Sheba. 1 Kings 10:1-13

5. Ziba. 2 Samuel 16:4

6. Asa. 1 Kings 5:13

7. Jezebel. 2 Kings 9:33-37

8. Zacchaeus. Luke 19:1-3

9. Silas. Acts 15:40

10. Titus. Titus 1:12

The Gospel of Luke was written to
THEOPHILUS.

JUST THE FACTS, MA'AM

Before an Israelite could offer a ram as a burnt offering, he had to wash its legs with water. Leviticus 1:9

When Joseph found out that Mary was pregnant, he wanted to divorce her quietly. Even though they were only engaged, that was the proper way to be dismissed from the obligation. Matthew 2:19

Joash was a mere seven years old when he became king. 2 Chronicles 24:1

? What is another name for Lake of Gennesaret?

The Sea of Galilee. Luke 5:1

Og, the king of Bashan, had an iron bed 13 feet long and 6 feet wide. Deuteronomy 3:11

Nazareth to Bethlehem is approximately 70 miles as the crow flies. As the donkey trots, it's about a three day trip.

Shallum was a ruler of Israel for only one month before he was assassinated by his successor. 2 Kings 15:13

It took Solomon 13 years to build his palace. It only took him seven years to build the temple. 1 Kings 6:38-7:1

CAMP RULES
(AT LEAST FOR THE ISRAELITES)

If you knock out your slave's tooth, you have to set him free.
Exodus 21:27

If you don't confine your ox that is known for killing people, and your ox kills somebody, you and your ox have to die. This is the final warning. Exodus 21:29

No eating tendons attached to the hip of an animal. Refer to your camp rule book about what happened to Jacob. Genesis 32:24ff.

Do not charge interest to a fellow camper. Only charge interest to foreigners. Deuteronomy 23:20

No tattoos. Leviticus 20:28

No tripping blind people. Leviticus 19:14

Please pick up all donkeys and oxen found lying in the road. Let's keep our camp clean. Deuteronomy 22:3

Don't eat things with wings. Leviticus 11:23

FOLLOW ME
MULTIPLE CHOICE

1. Jesus first found him fishing in the Sea of Galilee.
   a. Matthew   b. Andrew   c. Judas

2. He and his brother left their father to follow Jesus.
   a. Andrew   b. James   c. Thomas

3. Jesus healed his mother-in-law.
   a. Matthew   b. James   c. Peter

4. Jesus called him away from his job at the tax collector's booth.
   a. Matthew   b. Philip   c. James

5. He tried to walk with Jesus on the water.
   a. Bartholomew   b. Peter   c. John

6. This one gave Jesus a kiss but didn't do it out of love.
   a. Judas   b. Judas Iscariot   c. Thomas

7. Jesus gave him to Mary his mother before he died.
   a. Peter   b. James   c. John

8. He put his hand in Jesus' side after the Resurrection.
   a. Thomas   b. John   c. Peter

9. He had an early breakfast with Peter, Thomas, James, and John. Jesus cooked.
   a. Andrew   b. Philip   c. Nathanael

10. He baptized an Ethiopian he met on the road.
    a. Philip   b. Simon   c. Thomas

ANSWERS

1. Andrew. Matthew 4:18

2. James. Matthew 4:22

3. Peter. Matthew 4:15

4. Matthew. Matthew 9:9

5. Peter. Matthew 14:29

6. Judas Iscariot. Luke 22:47

7. John. John 19:20-27

8. Thomas. John 20:27

9. Nathanael. John 21:2

10. Philip. Acts 8:38

? Of the 12 spies who were sent to explore Canaan, which two gave invasion a thumbs up?

Joshua and Caleb. Numbers 14:6-9

ROYAL ROOSTS
WHAT COUNTRY DID THESE PEOPLE RULE?

1. Candace

2. Nebuchadnezzar

3. Cyrus

4. Shalmaneser

5. Pharaoh (pick one)

6. Nero

7. Ben-Hadad

8. Evil-Merodach

9. Sennacherib

10. Og

ANSWERS

1. Candace was queen of the Ethiopians. Acts 8:27

2. Nebuchadnezzar was king of Babylon. 2 Kings 24:1

3. Cyrus was king of Persia. 2 Chronicles 36:22

4. Shalmaneser was king of Assyria. 2 Kings 17:3

5. Pharaoh (all of them) was king of Egypt. Genesis 41:46

6. Nero was the emperor of Rome.

7. Ben-Hadad was king of Syria. 1 Kings 20:1

8. Evil-Merodach was another king of Babylon.
    2 Kings 25:27

9. Sennacherib was king of Assyria. 2 Chronicles 32:1

10. Og was king of Bashan. Numbers 21:33

REPEAT AFTER ME

When King David was old he was always cold, so he had a girl named Abishag to keep him warm and wait on him. 1 Kings 1:1-4

Three o'clock in the afternoon was prayertime in Paul's day. Acts 3:1

Samaria was built on a hill that was bought for about 150 pounds of silver. 1 Kings 16:24

• • • • • • • • • • • •

When Asa, King of Judah, was old he got diseased feet. 1 Kings 15:23

• • • • • • • • • • • •

Once when Paul was speaking a man named Eutychus who was sitting in a window fell asleep and plunged three stories to the ground. He died, but Paul brought him back to life. Acts 20:9-12

"It is more blessed to give than to receive..." is a quote from Jesus that He never actually said in the Bible. Acts 20:35

Manna means "what is it."

Israel (Jacob) told his sons to take pistachio nuts to the ruler (Joseph) in Egypt. Genesis 43:11

TAKE SEVEN

There were seven, or seven pairs, of every clean animal on the ark. Genesis 7:2-4

Jacob worked for Laban for seven years to marry Rachel, or so he thought. Genesis 29:18

Joshua and his army marched around Jericho seven times on the seventh day with seven priests blowing seven trumpets. Joshua 6:3-4

Samson had seven braids in his hair. Judges 16:13

Jesus fed "The Crowd" with seven loaves of bread. Matthew 15:34

Jesus drove seven demons from Mary Magdalene. Mark 16:9

Seven were chosen from the disciples to distribute food to widows. Acts 6:3

Joseph predicted seven years of abundance and seven years of famine in Egypt. Exodus 12:15

Passover lasted for seven days. Exodus 12:15

Naaman was healed of leprosy by dipping into the Jordan River seven times. 2 Kings 5:14

Of course there are more seven-things, but you get the point.

PAUL SLEPT HERE

1. At this house in Philippi.

2. On this street when he was blind.

3. Where he left his coat with Carpus.

4. Where he sang with Silas.

5. Where he was stoned and left for dead.

6. In Thessalonica where a nasty mob tried to hunt him down.

7. Where the disciples lowered him in a basket so he could get out of town.

8. On Malta where his ship ran aground.

9. Where he and Barnabas "shook the dust from their feet."

10. Where he made tents with Aquila and Priscilla.

WHERE PAUL SLEPT

1. Lydia's house. Acts 16:14-15

2. Straight Street. Acts 9:11

3. Troas. 2 Timothy 4:13

4. Jail in Philippi. Acts 16:25

5. Lystra. Acts 14:19

6. Jason's house. Acts 17:5

7. Damascus. Acts 9:25

8. Publius' house. Acts 28:7

9. Pisidian Antioch. Acts 13:13-51

10. Corinth. Acts 18:1-3

? The Book of Philemon is a post card from Paul to Philemon. On whose behalf was it written?

Onesimus, Philemon's runaway servant.

WHO SAID THIS?

1. "Look, Lord! Here and now I give half of my possessions to the poor. . . ."

2. "I have never eaten anything impure or unclean."

3. "I have sinned against the Lord."

4. "I baptize you with water for repentance."

5. "Now, O Lord, take away my life, for it is better for me to die than to live."

6. "But as for me and my household, we will serve the Lord."

7. "I appeal to Caesar."

8. "I have sinned for I have betrayed innocent blood."

9. "Your father and I have been anxiously searching for you."

10. "Come, see a man who told me everything I ever did."

WE SAID IT

1. Zacchaeus. Luke 19:8

2. Peter. Acts 10:14

3. David. 2 Samuel 12:13

4. John the Baptist. Matthew 3:11

5. Jonah. Jonah 4:3

6. Joshua. Joshua 24:15

7. Paul. Acts 25:11

8. Judas Iscariot. Matthew 27:4

9. Mary. Luke 2:48

10. The Samaritan woman. John 4:29

> **?** What is the last word in the Bible?
> *Amen. Revelation 22:21*

WHO'S CRYING NOW

Esau cried when Jacob got their father's blessing.
Genesis 27:38

Joseph cried when he saw Benjamin in Egypt.
Genesis 43:30

Benjamin cried when he saw Joseph in Egypt.
Genesis 45:14

Joseph cried when he saw Jacob in Egypt. Genesis 46:29

Jacob cried when he saw...Well, let's not get carried away.

Samson's wife cried to get the answer to his riddle.
Judges 14:16

King Joash cried at Elisha's death bed. 2 Kings 13:14

Esther cried while convincing King Xerxes to get rid of Haman. Esther 8:3

Baby Moses cried when Pharaoh's daughter found him.
Exodus 2:6

In the gross category. . .Isaiah said the sword of the Lord was covered with fat from rams' kidneys and blood from lambs and goats. Isaiah 34:6

Aaron and Hur were the two guys who held up Moses' hands while Joshua's army fought the Amalekites. As long as his hands were in the air, the Israelites were winning. Exodus 17:12

Jephthah and the Gileadites guarded a spot of land by asking Ephraimites to say "Shibboleth." They were killed if they couldn't say it correctly. Judges 12:5-6

> **?** Who is the "father of lies?"
> *The Devil. John 8:44*

When the Israelites won the battle with the Midianites, they got 675,000 sheep, 61,000 donkeys, and 32,000 "clean" women. Numbers 31:32-35

Jonathan once killed a huge man who had six fingers on each hand and six toes on each foot. 2 Samuel 21:20-21

Miriam, Moses' sister, had leprosy for seven days. Numbers 12:10

THE TEN COMMANDMENTS

Very simply, list the Ten Commandments. There's a Mercedes in it for you if you get them in order.

1. _____.

2. _____.

3. _____.

4. _____.

5. _____.

6. _____.

7. _____.

8. _____.

9. _____.

10. _____.

THE TEN COMMANDMENTS
IN ORDER
EXODUS 20:3-17

Just kidding about the Mercedes. Don't be so greedy.

1. You shall have no other gods before me.

2. You shall not make for yourself an idol.

3. You shall not misuse the name of the Lord your God.

4. Remember the Sabbath day by keeping it holy.

5. Honor your father and your mother.

6. You shall not murder.

7. You shall not commit adultery.

8. You shall not steal.

9. You shall not give false testimony against your neighbor.

10. You shall not covet anything belonging to your neighbor.

More Ten Commandment Stuff

2 Parts of Part 2

A: Which of the Ten Commandments are not mentioned in the New Testament, either by Jesus, Paul, or the Gospel writers?

1. _____.

2. _____.

3. _____.

4. _____.

Hint: There appear to be four.

B: What is the greatest commandment in the Law?
(This is not trivial, but it should make you think a bit.)

_____

_____

_____

ANSWERS TO 2 PARTS OF PART 2

A

1. You shall have no other gods before me. Exodus 20:3

2. You shall not make for yourself an idol. 20:4

3. You shall not misuse the name of the Lord your God. 20:7

4. Remember the Sabbath day by keeping it holy. 20:8

B

Matthew 22:37: Love the Lord your God
with all your heart and with all your soul
and with all your mind.

CASTING LOTS

During various times in the Bible, people cast lots to help them make decisions. They believed, in many cases, that the outcome was actually determined by God, so this is hardly a case for Atlantic City. A few examples:

The scapegoat was chosen that way. Leviticus 16:8

Joshua cast lots to distribute land to all the Israelite tribes. Joshua 18:10

Sailors cast lots to find out who was responsible for a big storm. It turned out to be Jonah. Jonah 1:7

The disciples cast lots to choose a replacement for Judas. Acts 1:26

The Israelites cast lots to figure out when each family was supposed to bring wood to burn at the altar. Nehemiah 10:34

Soldiers cast lots for Jesus' clothes. Matthew 27:35

David cast lots to choose heads of certain families who would minister. 1 Chronicles 24:5

Musicians cast lots to decide their responsibilities. 1 Chronicles 25:8

Lots were cast by families to choose gate keepers in Jerusalem. No wonder. Who would volunteer for the Dung gate, anyway? 1 Chronicles 26:3

GRACE NOTES

During the whole time the Israelites wandered around the desert, they never got swollen feet. Deuteronomy 8:4

The Ammonites were a stench in David's nostrils.
2 Samuel 10:6

Paul once healed a man who had dysentery. How nice of him. Acts 28:8

The next time you see a picture of Noah's family looking young and agile, look twice. Shem was 98 when the flood came. Genesis 11:10

Adam and Eve made the first clothes out of fig leaves.
Genesis 3:8

There are 12 books of the Bible that start with J.

Moses hit a rock and got water when he was just supposed to talk to it. That's why he wasn't allowed to move to Canaan. Numbers 20:13

Saul had a seance once led by a medium from Endor. They called up Samuel from the dead. Don't try this at home.
1 Samuel 28:11

WHODUNIT?
WHO RAISED THESE PEOPLE FROM THE DEAD?

1. The son of the widow at Zarephath.
   a. Elijah   b. Elisha   c. Jeremiah

2. The son of the Shunammite woman who sneezed seven times when he was brought back to life.
   a. Elijah   b. Elisha   c. Jeremiah

3. The only son of the widow of Nain.
   a. Paul   b. Peter   c. Jesus

4. The 12-year-old daughter of Jairus, a ruler of the synagogue.
   a. Peter   b. Jesus   c. Paul

5. Lazarus, who was called from the tomb after four days.
   a. Peter   b. Jesus   c. Paul

6. Tabitha (Dorcas) from Joppa.
   a. Peter   b. Jesus   c. Paul

7. Eutychus, the guy who went to sleep and fell out of a three-story window.
   a. Peter   b. Jesus   c. Paul

THEY DID!

1. Elijah. 1 Kings 17:17-23

2. Elisha. 2 Kings 4:32-35

3. Jesus. Luke 7:11-17

4. Jesus. Luke 8:40-56

5. Jesus. John 11:1-44

6. Peter. Acts 9:36-43

7. Paul. Acts 20:9-12

? Who were Jesus' brothers by birth, or half-birth?
James, Joseph, Jr., Simon, and Judas. Matthew 13:15

VERILY I SAY TO YOU

To whom was Jesus speaking when he said. . .

1. Come down immediately. I must stay at your house today.

2. Woman, why are you crying?

3. Didn't you know I had to be in my Father's house?

4. Before the rooster crows today, you will disown me three times.

5. Mary has chosen what is better, and it will not be taken away from her.

6. For God so loved the world that he gave his one and only Son, that whoever believes in him shall not perish but have eternal life.

7. Here is a true Israelite, in whom there is nothing false.

8. Come, follow me, and I will make you fishers of men.

9. Are you still so dull?

10. You would have no power over me if it were not given to you from above.

ANSWERS

1. Zaccheus. Luke 9:5

2. Mary Magdalene. John 20:15

3. Joseph and Mary. Luke 2:49

4. Peter. Luke 22:61

5. Martha. Luke 10:42

6. Nicodemus. John 3:16

7. Nathanael. John 1:47

8. Peter and Andrew. Matthew 4:19

9. The disciples. Matthew 16:13

10. Pontius Pilate. John 19:11

? To whom was 3 John addressed?
Somebody named Gaius, John's friend. 3 John 1

MEDIUM RARE

Have you seen the writing on the wall? King Belshazzar did. When he was drinking out of a goblet from Jerusalem's temple, a hand wrote a message on his wall.
Daniel 5:5

Moses smashed the tablets of the Ten Commandments, so God had to make another set. Exodus 34:1

The Israelites wore tassels on their clothes to remind them of God's commandments. Numbers 15:38

The city of Ephesus was the guardian of the temple of Artemis, a fertility god. Acts 19:35

• • • • • • • • • • • •

*David pretended to be insane once by marking
up a door and drooling all over his face.
1 Samuel 21:13*

• • • • • • • • • • • •

When the Israelites first checked out Canaan, they found grapevines so full it took two men to carry a single cluster.
Numbers 13:23

A beautiful, indiscreet woman is like a gold ring in a pig's snout. Proverbs 11:22

Jacob made the coat that he gave to Joseph, his favorite son.
Genesis 37:3

DOWN FOR THE COUNT
(OF 12!)

Ishmael had 12 sons who were tribal rulers. Genesis 17:20

Jacob had 12 sons, too. You know who they were.
Genesis 49:28

The Sea in Solomon's temple stood on 12 bulls. 1 Kings 7:25

Elisha plowed with 12 yoke of oxen. 1 Kings 19:19

Jesus called 12 disciples. Matthew 10:1

There were 12 baskets full of leftovers when Jesus fed a
crowd of people. Matthew 14:20

The New Jerusalem will have 12 gates guarded by twelve
angels. Revelation 21:12

Moses sent 12 spies into Canaan. Numbers 13:1-15

A Levite cut his dead concubine up into 12 pieces, one for
each tribe of Israel. That wasn't very nice. Judges 19:29

JUDGMENT DAY

Complete the acrostic with the names of the major judges. O.K., so it's misspelled. God must not have known any qualified people with U names.

1. J _ _ _ _ _ _ _

2. O _ _ _ _ _ _ _

3. D _ _ _ _ _ _ _

4. G _ _ _ _ _

5. E _ _ _

6. S _ _ _ _ _ _

ANSWERS

1. Jephthah, the one who sacrificed his daughter.

2. Othniel, Caleb's little brother who got Israel away from Mesopotamia.

3. Deborah, the woman who accompanied Barak into battle.

4. Gideon, the one who distributed Bibles. Just kidding.

5. Ehud, who killed fat King Eglon with a home made sword.

6. Samson, the strong one with long hair.

STAND BY YOUR MAN

Match the women to the men they were either married to or associated with.

1. Abigail   A. Abraham

2. Abital   B. David

3. Ahinoam   C. Jacob

4. Bathsheba

5. Bilhah

6. Eglah

7. Hagar

8. Haggith

9. Keturah

10. Leah

11. Maacah

12. Michal

13. Rachel

14. Sarah

15. Zilpah

ANSWERS

1. Abigail and David

2. Abital and David

3. Ahinoam and David

4. Bathsheba and David

5. Bilhah and Jacob

6. Eglah and David

7. Hagar and Abraham

8. Haggith and David

9. Keturah and Abraham

10. Leah and Jacob

11. Maacah and David

12. Michal and David

13. Rachel and Jacob

14. Sarah and Abraham

15. Zilpah and Jacob

HAVE A CLUE

Myrrh is a gum resin.

Frankincense is a combination of gum and spices.

Flux is the same as violent dysentery. Acts 28:8

A testament, as in Old and New, is a statement of belief and/or evidence that something happened.

An ebenezer is a memorial stone. 1 Samuel 4:1

The next time you wear a shawl, you will be wearing a wimple. Ruth 3:15

Papyrus is writing paper made from a papyrus plant.

Cherubim are winged creatures that are half man and half animal.

Seraphim is the plural of the angel-types that Isaiah talked about.

PILLARS OF SALT
(OR A LOT ABOUT NOTHING)

Gamaliel was a famous teacher in Jerusalem who taught Paul everything he knew about a few things. Acts 22:3

Obadiah hid 100 prophets in caves and gave them food and water. 1 Kings 18:4

When Sennacherib and his army were camped outside Jerusalem one night, the angel of the Lord quietly killed 185,000 of them. Have a nice evening. 2 Kings 19:35

Abraham wasn't circumcised until he was 99 years old. Genesis 17:24

The next time you say, "Eat, drink and be merry," remember it was a fool who said it first. Luke 12:19

If Samson loved his wife enough to kill for her, why did he call her a cow? Read Judges 14:18

When the Benjamites were short on women, they went to a festival where each man caught one to take home. Judges 21:23

Isaac means "he laughed."

SAY IT AGAIN, SAM

Who said. . .

1. Why have you disturbed me by bringing me up?

2. How can a man be born when he is old?

3. I am innocent of this man's blood.

4. No. You shall never wash my feet.

5. Jesus, remember me when you come into your kingdom.

6. He must become greater; I must become less.

7. Rabbi, I want to see.

8. I'll draw water for your camels, too, until they have finished drinking.

9. Samson, the Philistines are upon you!

10. You will not surely die.

ANSWERS

1. Samuel, when Saul called him up from the grave. 1 Samuel 28:15

2. Nicodemus to Jesus. John 3:4

3. Pontius Pilate. Matthew 27:24

4. Peter. John 13:8

5. The thief on the cross. Luke 23:42

6. John the Baptist. John 3:30

7. Bartimaeus. Mark 10:51

8. Rebekah. Genesis 24:44

9. Delilah. Judges 16:9

10. The serpent. Genesis 3:4

• • • • • • • • • • • • •

*God made the shadow on a sundial go back
ten steps as a sign to Hezekiah. 2 Kings 20:11*

THE GOOD, THE BAD,
AND THE ABYSMAL

A few kings are listed below. Your job, should you decide to accept it: Which ones did right and which did evil in the eyes of the Lord? Then choose which kingdom they ruled, Israel or Judah.

1. Rehoboam

2. Asa

3. Nadab

4. Jehoshaphat

5. Omri

6. Ahaziah

7. Jehoahaz

8. Ahaz

9. Amaziah

10. Manasseh

ANSWERS

1. Rehoboam was evil in Judah.

2. Asa was good in Judah.

3. Nadab was evil in Israel.

4. Jehoshaphat was good in Judah.

5. Omri was evil in Israel.

6. Ahaziah was evil in Israel.

7. Jehoahaz was evil in Israel.

8. Ahaz was good in Judah.

9. Amaziah was good in Judah.

10. Manasseh was evil in Judah.

SOME MORE THREES

The wisemen gave baby Jesus three things—gold, frankincense, and myrrh. Matthew 2:11

The Holy Place in the Tabernacle had three things–the lampstand, the wood table, and the consecrated bread. Hebrews 9:2

Noah's three sons were Shem, Ham, and Japheth. Genesis 7:13

Job had three "comforting" friends. Job 4:1; 8:1; 11:1

Daniel had three friends—Shadrach, Meshach, and Abednego. Daniel 1:6

Noah's ark had three stories. Genesis 6:16

Esau had three wives—Judith, Basemath, and Mahalath. Genesis 26:34; 28:9

Jochebed's three children were Aaron, Miriam, and Moses. Various places in Exodus.

MORE PILLARS OF SALT

Esau was sometimes called Edom, which means red.
Genesis 25:30

In a battle, fighting men from Judah caught a man named
Adoni-Bezek and cut off his fingers and big toes. Judges 1:6

There are 590 words in Obadiah. You can count them if you
want to.

When Nebuchadnezzar went insane, he grew claws like a
bird, feathers like an eagle, and ate grass like a cow.
Daniel 4:33

While Ishmael lived in the desert with his mom, he learned
to be an archer. Genesis 21:20

Samson killed more people when he died than he did when
he lived. Judges 16:30

Abraham had slaves. Genesis 17:27

? Recite Hezekiah 3:17

Hezekiah was a king, not a book, silly.

108

THE 12 TRIBES OF ISRAEL

Place the names of the tribes of Israel in their designated land allotments. There are, as you know, only 12 tribes and 14 sections of land, so think hard.

MAP ANSWERS

1. Asher

2. Naphtali

3. Dan

4. Manasseh

5. Zebulun

6. Issachar

7. Manasseh, again.

8. Gad

9. More of Dan

10. Ephraim

11. Benjamin

12. Judah

13. Simeon

14. Reuben

MATCH THE 'ITES

1. Gilonite
2. Tishbite
3. Canaanite
4. Hittite
5. Jebusite
6. Ammonite
7. Moabite
8. Amorite
9. Levite
10. Gileadite

A. Uriah
B. Araunah
C. Mamre
D. Aaron
E. Elijah
F. Ahithopel
G. Shua
H. Jephthah
I. Nahash
J. Ruth

MATCHED 'ITES

1. F. Ahithopel, David's counselor who sided with Absalom. 2 Samuel 15:12

2. E. Elijah, the prophet who was taken to heave. 1 Kings 17:1

3. G. Shua, Judah's father-in-law. Genesis 38:2

4. A. Uriah, Bathsheba's departed husband. 2 Samuel 11:6

5. B. Araunah. David saw the Angel of the Lord on his threshing floor. 1 Chronicles 21:15

6. I. Nahash, who wanted to remove the right eye of everyone in Jabesh Gilead. 1 Samuel 11:1

7. J. Ruth. Ruth 1:4

8. C. Mamre, an associate of Abraham. Genesis 14:13

9. D. Aaron, Moses' brother. Exodus 4:14

10. H. Jephthah, the judge who fought the Ammonites. Judges 11:1

LOOK UNTO THE HILLS

When the Israelites were about to possess Canaan, they were to give blessings from Mount Gerizim and curses from Mount Ebal. Deuteronomy 11:29

Aaron died on Mount Hor. Numbers 20:29

Moses saw all of the Promised Land from Mount Nebo. Deuteronomy 34:1

Elijah proved the power of God in a contest with Baal worshipers on Mount Carmel. 1 Kings 18:19

Solomon built the temple on Mount Moriah. 2 Chronicles 3:1

Jesus gave the Beatitudes from a mountainside. You know—the Sermon on the Mount. Matthew 5:1

Abraham almost sacrificed Isaac on a mountain in Moriah. Genesis 22:2

God gave Moses the Ten Commandments on Mount Sinai. Exodus 19:3

Etc.

King Jehoiakim was really Eliakim. An Egyptian Pharoah changed his name. 2 Kings 23:34

Jesus called James and John "Sons of Thunder." Mark 3:17

As a curse, Joshua made the Gibeonites serve as woodcutters and water carriers for the Israelites. Joshua 9:23

• • • • • • • • • • • •

It takes 11 days to go from Horeb to Kadesh Barnea by the Mount Seir road. They must not have had a jeep. Deuteronomy 1:2

• • • • • • • • • • • •

The new earth won't have oceans. Revelation 21:1

Moses had two sons, Gershom and Eliezer. Exodus 18:3

Gehazi, a servant, lied to Elisha and got leprosy.
2 Kings 5:27

God killed Er, Tamar's first husband, because he was wicked. Genesis 38:7

Daniel was renamed Belteshazzar by the Babylonians.
Daniel 1:7

ARE YOU MY MOTHER?

Their fathers are famous Bible characters, but do you know their mothers? Fill in the blanks.

1. Solomon, David and _____ son.

2. Samuel, Elkanah and _____ son.

3. Joseph, Jacob and _____ son.

4. Judah, Jacob and _____ son.

5. Obed, Boaz and _____ son.

6. Adonijah, David and _____ son.

7. Ahaziah, Ahab and _____ son.

8. Ishmael, Abraham and _____ son.

9. Jonathan, Saul and _____ son.

10. Eliphaz, Esau and _____ son.

ANSWERS

1. Bathsheba. 2 Samuel 12:24

2. Hannah. 1 Samuel 1:20

3. Rachel. Genesis 30:22-24

4. Leah. Genesis 29:35

5. Ruth. Ruth 4:17

6. Haggith. 1 Kings 1:5

7. Athaliah. 2 Kings 8:26

8. Hagar. Genesis 16:15

9. Ahinoam. 1 Samuel 14:49-50

10. Adah. Genesis 36:4

? Which "Marys" were at the cross?

Mary, Jesus' mother; Mary Magdalene; Mary, James' mother; and Mary, Clopas' wife.
John 19:25; Mark 15:40

Sibling Rivalry?

Some are brothers, some are sisters, some are half of each.

1. Jesus called them when they were fishing.

2. One was a farmer and one was a shepherd.

3. One brother had the other one killed for violating their sister.

4. Jacob might have called these sisters the beauty and the beast.

5. These twins exchanged a birthright for a bowl of stew.

6. Jesus called these sons of Zebedee, too.

7. They were half-brothers whose descendants fought on a regular basis.

8. This married couple tended to laugh at the wrong times.

9. These brothers of Ham covered up their dad under exposing circumstances.

10. These sisters of Lazarus were very attentive to Jesus.

ANSWERS

1. Simon Peter and Andrew. Matthew 4:18

2. Cain and Abel. Genesis 4:1-2

3. Absalom and Ammon. 2 Samuel 13

4. Rachel and Leah. Genesis 29:16

5. Jacob and Esau. Genesis 25:22-36

6. James and John. Matthew 4:21

7. Isaac and Ishmael. Genesis 16:15; 21:3

8. Abraham and Sarah. Genesis 20:12

9. Shem and Japheth. Genesis 9:23

10. Mary and Martha. John 12:1-3

 Saul had a son named Jonathan, of course.
But can you name his four other children?
Ishvi, Malki-Shua, Merab, and Michal. 1 Samuel 17:4

DO YOU WANT TO KNOW
A SECRET?

Goliath was over nine feet tall. 1 Samuel 17:4

Before a girl could be presented to King Xerxes, she had to put up with 12 months of beauty treatments. Esther 2:12

The Philistines offered gold rats as a guilt offering. Thanks a lot! 1 Samuel 6:18

Boaz gave Ruth and Naomi a load of barley as a present. Ruth 3:15

Samuel's mother made him a little robe every year while he was living with Eli. 1 Samuel 2:19

Jesus was trying to be alone to mourn the death of John the Baptist when the crowd of 5000-plus found him. Surprise! Matthew 14:13

Moses was more humble than anybody. Numbers 12:3

David's bodyguard Benaiah killed a lion in the snow. 1 Chronicles 11:23

TENFOLD

God gave Ten Commandments. Exodus 20:3-17

David took ten loaves of bread and ten cheeses to his brothers who were fighting the Philistines. 1 Samuel 17:17

There were ten basins, ten gold candlesticks, and ten tables in the temple. 2 Chronicles 4:6-8

Haman, from the book of Esther, had ten sons. Esther 9:14

A ten-acre vineyard will produce only a bath of wine, or about six gallons. Isaiah 5:10

Jesus told a story about ten virgins who were waiting for the bridegroom. Matthew 25:1

Then He told about a woman who had ten silver coins and lost one. Luke 15:8

Then He told another one about a man who gave ten minas to ten servants. Luke 19:13

Jesus healed ten lepers. Luke 17:12

THE 2000 LITTLE PIGS

(AND OTHER TRUE STORIES!)

Once Jesus called demons out of a man and sent them into a herd of about 2000 pigs. Mark 5:13

When the kings of Sodom and Gomorrah ran away from their enemies, they got stuck in some tar pits. Genesis 14:10

After Haman was hanged on the gallows, King Xerxes hanged his sons, too. Esther 9:14

• • • • • • • • • • • •

Aaron's hunchbacked descendants couldn't offer food to God. Leviticus 21:20

• • • • • • • • • • • •

Solomon's throne had six steps and a gold footstool attached to it. 2 Chronicles 9:18

Some city officials put Jeremiah in a mud hole to starve to death. Jeremiah 38:6

There are seven different Jeremiahs in the Bible. 1 Chronicles 5:24; 12:4, 10, 13; 2 Kings 23:30; Jeremiah 1:1; 35:3

When God needed to punish David, he gave him three choices: three years of famine, three months of enemy pursuit, or three days of plague. Which would you choose? 2 Samuel 24:13

Jephthah's mother was a prostitute. Judges 11:1

David's son Absalom conspired to get the throne from his father. 2 Samuel 15

Gideon had 71 sons. Judges 8:30

> ? Elijah didn't die, as you know. Who else was "taken away?"
>
> Enoch, Methuselah's dad. Genesis 5:24

Samson killed a thousand men with a donkey's jawbone. Judges 15:16

Paul circumcised Timothy. Acts 16:3

Abraham sent 318 men to rescue Lot from captivity. Genesis 14:14-16

God struck Uzzah dead when he touched the ark of the covenant. The poor guy was trying to keep the ark from falling off its cart. 2 Samuel 6:7

Shamgar, one of the judges, killed 600 Philistines with an oxgoad. Judges 3:31

WOW YOUR FRIENDS WITH MORE BIBLE TRIVIA AND CLEAN JOKES!

The Fun Book of Bible Trivia II by Robyn Martins and *500 Clean Jokes and Humorous Stories and How to Tell Them* by Rusty Wright & Linda Raney Wright offer hours of fun for all ages!

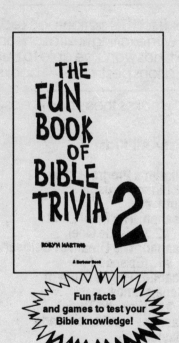

Fun facts and games to test your Bible knowledge!

Jokes and stories and tips on how to tell them successfully!

Available at Christian Book Stores Everywhere.
or order from
Barbour and Company, Inc.
P.O. Box 719
Uhrichsville, Ohio 44683

$3.97 each retail, plus $1.00 for postage and handling per order.